Mr. PANTS

TRICK OR FEET!

WORDS BY
SCOTT McCORMICK

PICTURES BY
R. H. LAZZELL

SCHOLASTIC INC.

D0208051

FOR MY WIFE, WITH, YOU KNOW, LOVE AND STUFF.
"... CLOUDS ..."   —S.M.

FOR DENNIS AND MEL, WHO WERE ALWAYS AN
INSPIRATION TO ME.   —R.H.L.

ISBN 978-1-338-09927-0

Text copyright © 2015 by Scott McCormick. Pictures copyright © 2015 by R. H. Lazzell. All rights
reserved. Published by Scholastic Inc., 557 Broadway, New York, NY 10012, by arrangement with
Dial Books for Young Readers, an imprint of Penguin Young Readers Group, a division of Penguin
Random House LLC. SCHOLASTIC and associated logos are trademarks and/or registered
trademarks of Scholastic Inc.

12 11 10 9 8 7 6 5 4 3 2 1   16 17 18 19 20 21

Printed in the U.S.A.   40

First Scholastic printing, September 2016

Designed by Jennifer Kelly
Text set in Archer

CONTENTS

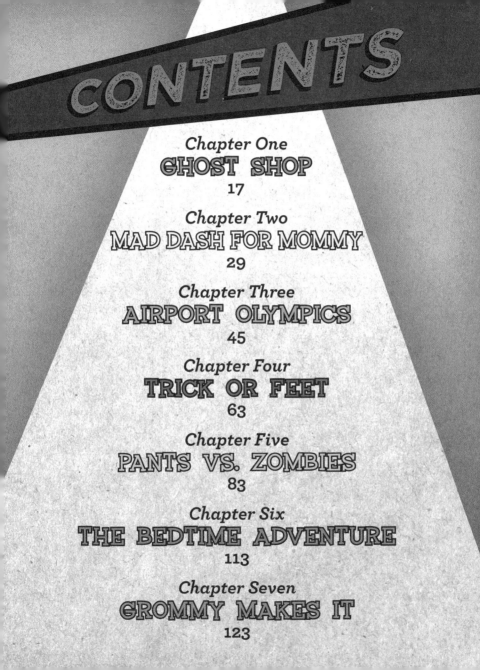

Guys! I just heard on the TV: The big Halloween Zombie Tag game is happening this weekend!

7

"Moi?" says Fuffles.
THE COOKIE CAPER
That's my favorite!
THE COOKIE CAPER
YAWN
"Well, you do try to steal cookies all the time," his sister said. But he just can't help himself, can he?
So he climbs up on the counter but Mom catches him.
THE COOKIE CAPER

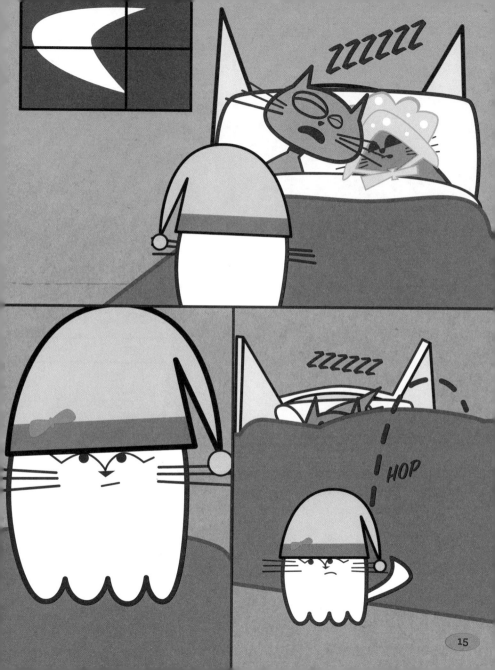

Chapter One:
GHOST SHOP

HALLOWEEN COSTUMES
THIS WAY

Faster, Mom, or all the zombie costumes will be gone!

And the year before that I got sick, so I haven't been trick-or-treating in three years! I don't care what happens: I am trick-or-treating this year.
Me too!
I haven't even told you my big surprise.
What is it?
Well, I know I've been super-busy with work lately . . . But now that my launch is over, I decided to book us a last-minute trip. So, this year we're going to do Halloween at Papa and DeeDee's!

21

Or here . . . You could be a lawyer zombie! Oooh! Super-scary!

Come on, work with me here.

A lawyer zombie?

Makeup?

I have a bad feeling about this Halloween . . .

Chapter Two:
MAD DASH FOR MOMMY

e next day

And a freak Halloween snow storm has hit the Northeast, blanketing the area with several inches of snow . . .

WEATHER ALERT

TERMINAL Z

BONK

SPLAT

DOWN

43

Chapter Three: AIRPORT OLYMPICS

Welp. We're gonna be here a while. What do you guys want to do?

ELEVATOR 2000

49

53

SPIN!

67

75

Look: She's slow. We don't have to panic.
Yeah, but that's how zombies get you. They lull you to sleep and the next thing you know . . .
GRAINNNNNSSSSSSSSSS
Eeep!

93

105

This way!
Rules, schmules! This is Zombie Tag!
I thought you said we couldn't jump over the people mover . . .
I like this guy!
PEOPLE MOVER 2000
This looks like the end!

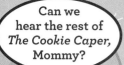

Can we hear the rest of *The Cookie Caper,* Mommy?

No way. I'm not reading that book.

Why on earth not?

You know why! This time I'm reading whatever book *I* want to read.

Like this scientific journal!

Rocket

Mwa-ha-ha-ha-ha! This is gonna put YOU to sleep quicker than you can say "Methanogenesis"!

It IS Rocket Science

Do your worst.

All right, tough guy. Read it and sleep!

Our new engine will operate at a liquid oxygen and kerosene mixture ratio of 2.57 to 1 . . .

. . . to produce the 36 meganewtons of thrust needed to reach low Earth orbit.

117

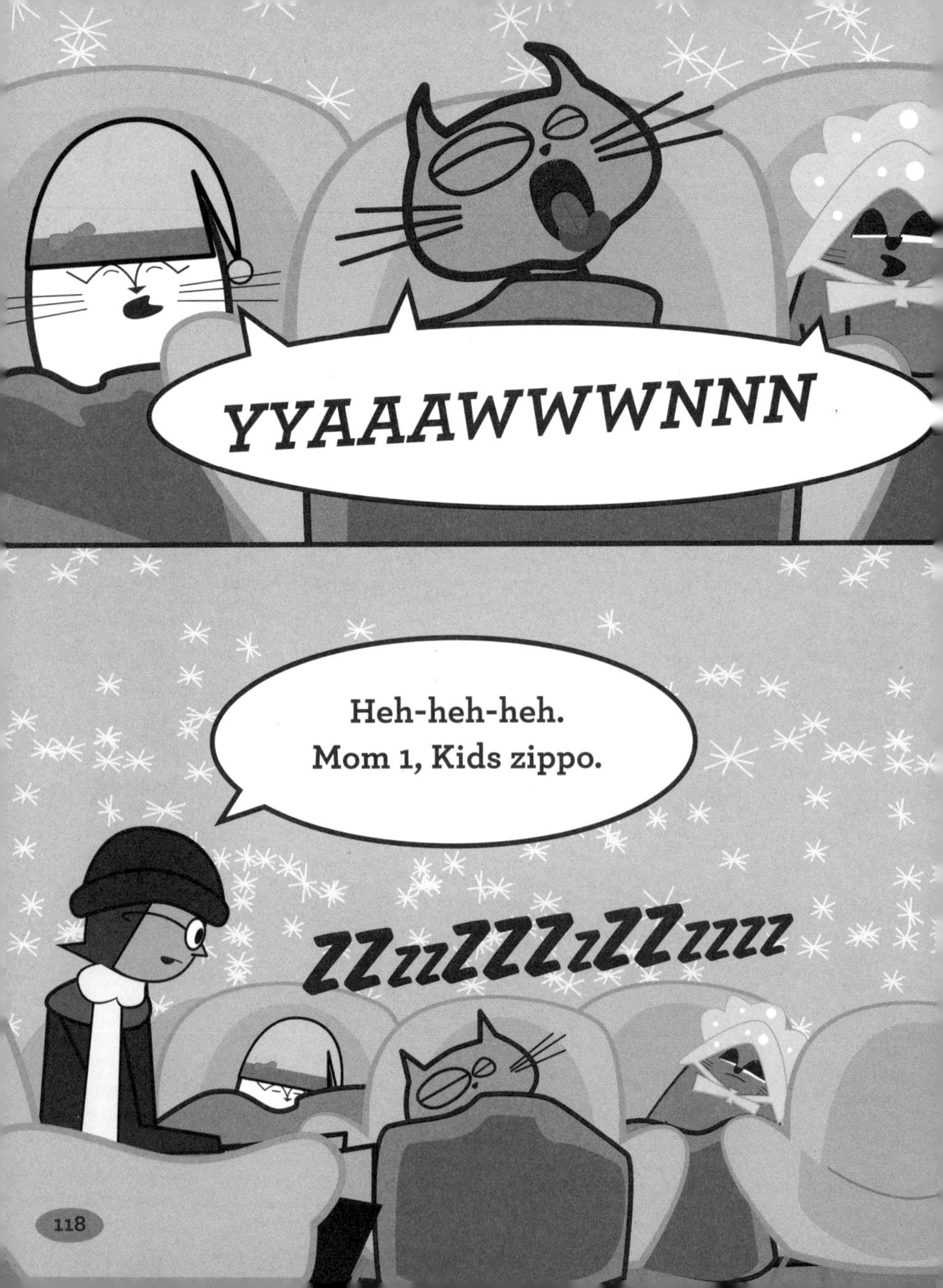
YYAAAWWWNNN
Heh-heh-heh.
Mom 1, Kids zippo.
ZZzzZZZzZZzzzz

About the Authors:

Don't try playing vegan zombie tag with SCOTT MCCORMICK in an airport. He's already scouted out all the cool hiding places. But if you do—and if you're lucky enough to tag him—he's got dibs on saying "triticale." Scott lives in North Carolina.

R. H. LAZZELL enjoys the changing leaves in the autumn and watching spooky movies. He is currently running from zombies in New Jersey.